Printed and Published in Great Britain by D. C. THOMSON & CO., LTD.,
185 Fleet Street, London, EC4A 2HS
© D. C. THOMSON & CO., LTD., 1985.
ISBN 0 85116 323 8

BULLY BEEF and CHIPS

IN "DING-DONG BATTLES"

HO-HO!

SNARL!

I'M LOOKING FOR CHIPS. I WANT TO BASH HIM BEFORE I GO TO SCHOOL!

AH, THERE HE IS, WAITING TO BOARD THE SCHOOL BUS! HOI, CHIPS!

BUS STOP

OH, CRUMBS! IT'S BEEFY!

COME HERE, CHIPS!

NO FEAR!

DING! DONG!

HA-HA! SAVED BY THE BELL!

VROOM!

SNARL!

At the school gates—

—AND I RANG THE BELL AND ESCAPED.

TEE-HEE! SO BEEFY MISSED THE BUS.

HO-HO!

GURR! I HAD TO RUN ALL THE WAY. NOW TO BASH YOU.

OH, NO!

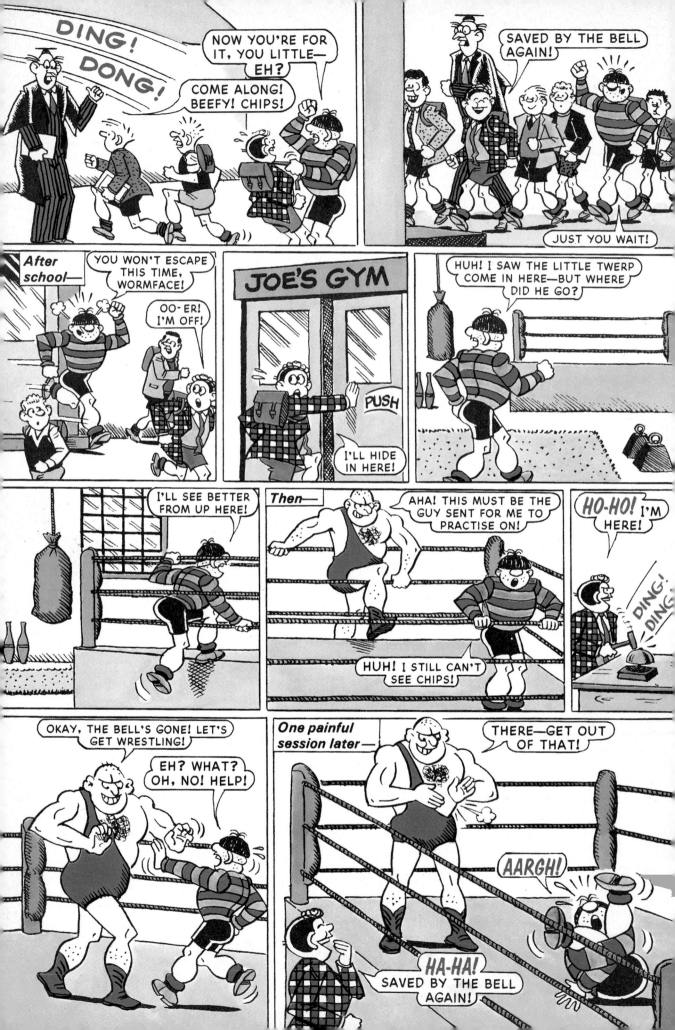

KORKY the CAT

TOM TUM

I EXPECT YOU WANT TO KNOW HOW I GOT THIS BLACK EYE, READERS!

WELL, IT ALL STARTED IN CLASS—

WHAT DO YOU KNOW ABOUT GEOMETRY SHAPES, TOM TUM?

CRUNCH! CHOMP!

SQUARE CRISPS

TODAY I HAD SOME SQUARE CRISPS.

CRUNCH! CRUNCH!

THEN HAD A FEW SUGAR CUBES!

SLURP!

AND ON MY WAY TO SCHOOL I HAD AN ICE-CREAM CONE.

VERY GOOD, TOM TUM. NOW, WOULD YOU LIKE SOMETHING ROUND?

YES PLEASE, SIR!

COME WITH ME!

MAYBE IT'S A CHEESE ROUND!

AND THAT'S HOW I GOT THIS BLACK EYE . . .

OUCH!

BOP!

. . . THE SCHOOL BOXING CHAMP BOXED A ROUND WITH ME!

THE weirdest helicopter in the whole world—that's Brassneck, the metal boy with the rotating leg! Now read on, to find out why he is taking a squirming squire for a free flight.

Our story starts earlier that day, when the Brand family arrived at their Scottish holiday home . . .

THIS MUST BE THE HOUSE WE RENTED! IT'S A BEAUTIFUL-LOOKING PLACE!

Brassneck volunteered to unload the family's luggage.

THIS WON'T TAKE LONG!

But then—

OUT! HOW DARE YOU WALK INTO MY HOUSE!

BUT THIS IS OUR HOLIDAY HOME!

BOOT!

THAT'S THE HOUSE I RENT OUT TO SCRUFFY TOURISTS! I'M SQUIRE DUFF AND I DON'T WANT YOU PEOPLE DISTURBING ME!

WHAT AN UNPLEASANT FELLOW!

THIS PLACE IS A BIT CRAMPED, BUT I SUPPOSE IT WILL DO!

In the boys' room—

LET'S GO OUT AND HAVE A GAME OF CRICKET, BRASSNECK!

GREAT IDEA, CHARLEY!

THWACK!

YOWCH!

ERK! SOUNDS AS IF OUR BALL'S HIT SOMEONE!

IT'S THE SQUIRE! RUN, BRASSNECK!

YOUNG VANDALS!

Meanwhile, Dad Brand decided to go fishing.

IT'S LUCKY THERE'S A LOCH JUST BESIDE OUR HOUSE!

IN YOU GO!

GULP!

I'LL TAKE YOU BACK TO DRY LAND!

OH, NO! MY WATCH MUST HAVE COME OFF WHEN I LANDED IN THE WATER!

DON'T WORRY, MR BRAND! I'LL FIND YOUR WATCH FOR YOU!

HERE IT IS! MY METAL DETECTOR NOSE NEVER FAILS!

CHARLEY'S DAD WILL BE PLEASED . . . HEY! WHAT'S THIS?

AMAZING! A WHOLE HOUSE ON THE BOTTOM OF THE LOCH!

Back on dry land—

THIS AREA WAS FLOODED TO MAKE A RESERVOIR! THAT HOUSE MUST HAVE BEEN COVERED BY WATER AT THAT TIME!

SO THAT'S WHAT HAPPENED!

Shortly—

LET'S TEACH THAT SNEAKY SQUIRE A LESSON!

HERE HE COMES, BUT DON'T WORRY! HE WON'T HAVE A CHANCE TO TOPPLE OUR BOAT THIS TIME!

WHIRR!

NOW TO USE MY HELICOPTER LEG!

IT'S NOT TROUT I'M FISHING FOR, SQUIRE!

EH?

That evening—

THE TV DOESN'T WORK TOO WELL AND IT DOESN'T HAVE A REMOTE CONTROL CHANNEL CHANGER LIKE OUR SET AT HOME!

NO PROBLEM, DAD! I'LL FIX UP BRASSNECK SO YOU CAN USE HIS COMPUTER BRAIN AS A CHANNEL CHANGER!

THANKS, CHARLEY! THIS WORKS REALLY WELL!

CLICK

I'LL TRY ANOTHER CHANNEL . . .

CLICK!

. . .NO, I DON'T LIKE THAT SHOW . . .

CLICK!

. . .WONDER WHAT'S ON FOUR . . .

CLICK!

. . .NOPE! DON'T LIKE THAT EITHER . . .

CLICK!

I CAN'T STAND THIS ANY LONGER! I HAVEN'T HAD A MINUTE'S PEACE SINCE WE ARRIVED, BUT I KNOW WHERE I CAN HAVE A QUIET SEAT!

DESPERATE DAWG

DOGGIE PATCH SPORTS MEETING.

I'M PRACTISING FOR THE SPRINT AT THE SPORTS MEETING! GIVE ME A STARTING SIGNAL, LADS!

OKAY! READY... STEADY...

...GO!

WAH!

WHAM!

EH?

EEK!

SHERIFF!

LET ME DOWN, YOU TWIT!

HO-HO! PITY THERE ISN'T A PIGGY-BACK RACE!

Then—

THE SHERIFF WARNED ME OFF THE SPRINT, SO I'M GOING IN FOR THE HURDLES!

GREAT IDEA—PRACTISING WITH GARDEN FENCES!

I'LL FILL A FEW POTS WITH SOIL FOR MY BULBS!

OH, DEAR!

SPLAT!

UMF!

SNARL! NO MORE HURDLING—YOU CLUMSY TWIT!

The Smasher

IF YOU WANT TO EARN MORE POCKET MONEY, YOU CAN DO THE VACUUM-CLEANING WHILE I'M OUT SHOPPING, SMASHER.

EH?

BAH! WHAT AN INSULT—ASKING ME TO DO SUCH A SOPPY JOB!

But, later—

HEH-HEH! HERE COMES MR WIMPLE WITH HIS NEW HAIRDO!

EEK! MY WIG!

SUCK!

TEE-HEE!

"TOUPEE" OR NOT "TOUPEE"? THAT IS THE QUESTION!

GRR!

GIVE ME BACK MY WIG!

ALRIGHT! KEEP YOUR HAIR ON!

GRAB

Later—

AH! ANOTHER VICTIM!

YUM-YUM!

YAHOO!

TRIP!

HO-HO! ENJOY YOUR TRIP?

OOF!

CRUMP!

IT'S TIME I DID SOME VACUUM-CLEANING—CAN'T HAVE UNTIDY PAVEMENTS!

SUCK!

SLURP! LOVELY TOFFEES!

THE BURRD

WINKER WATSON

WHAT'S all this? It looks like Winker Watson, the famous schoolboy prankster, has got the upper hand over his old enemy, bad-tempered Form Master, Mr Clarence Creep, of Greytowers School! But where did the elephant come from? Well, a circus had pitched its Big Top next to the school, and that gave Winker the chance for this amazing adventure.

HELP!

It all started when a football team list went up on the notice board.

LOOK, WINKER! YOU'RE IN THE TEAM!

NOTICES

GREYTOWERS XI
V. THE CIRCUS
1. BANKS JUNIOR
2. SMITH MINOR
3. JONES
4. WILKINS
5. MR. EUCLID
6. MARSH
7. HEADMASTER
8. HODDLE JUNIOR
9. WATSON
10. TROTT
11. BARNET

AND SO ARE YOU, TROTTY!

The circus folk had challenged the Greytowers pupils and staff to a friendly football match and there was a free feast for the teams afterwards.

LET'S HAVE A PRACTICE MATCH!

Then Creepy spotted the notice, and he wasn't too pleased.

NOTICES

GREYTOWERS XI
V THE CIRCUS
1. BANKS JUNIOR
2. SMITH MINOR
3. JONES
4. WILKINS
5 MR EUCLID
6 MARSH
7. HEADMASTER
8. HODDLE JUNIOR
9 WATSON
10. TROTT
11. BARNET

WHAT'S THIS? WATSON'S IN THE TEAM, BUT I'M NOT. I'LL HAVE TO DO SOMETHING ABOUT THAT.

The crafty teacher soon came up with a nasty plan.

IDEA!

IF BY CHANCE WATSON WAS TOO TIRED TO PLAY, I COULD TAKE HIS PLACE. THEN I COULD JOIN IN THE FREE FEED— I KNOW HOW TO TIRE HIM OUT.

So—

WATSON! MOVE ALL THE LOGS FROM THE WOODPILE OVER TO THE FURNACE.

CHANGING ROOMS ➡

Winker had a word with his pal, Micki, the circus owner's son.

SO THAT'S WHAT I WOULD LIKE YOU TO DO, MICKI! CAN YOU FIX IT?

NO PROBLEM, WINKER!

So, when Creepy went to see how Winker was doing, he got a jumbo-sized shock.

GASP! AN ELEPHANT! I MUST PUT A STOP TO THIS!

But Creepy had arrived too late. Bimbo the elephant had already done the work!

REMOVE THIS BRUTE AT ONCE!

JAB!

FURNACES KEEP OUT!

The nasty teacher quickly had another idea. If he couldn't tire Winker out, he'd keep him working, right through the whole of the game!

THE QUAD IS AN ABSOLUTE MESS OF WOOD CHIPS! CLEAN IT UP AT ONCE!

BUT THAT'LL TAKE AGES!

WHAT A SHAME!

BAH! I'LL MISS THE GAME AGAINST THE CIRCUS, UNLESS I GET A HELPING HAND OR TWO!

Shortly—

I MUST POP ALONG AND SEE HOW WATSON IS DOING. I EXPECT HE'LL ONLY HAVE DONE A SMALL CORNER OF THE QUAD SO FAR!

But another big surprise awaited Creepy.

GASP! WHAT'S THIS? THE QUAD IS ALMOST COMPLETELY TIDIED UP. BUT HOW?

GANGWAY, SIR!

JEEPERS! AN OCTOPUS!

BRUSH!

BRUSH!

BRUSH!

BRUSH!

Creepy rapped out more orders.

THAT'S ENOUGH, WATSON! NOW PUT THE BRUSHES BACK IN THE JANITOR'S SHED!

JANITOR KEEP OUT

SLAM!

At the shed, Creepy sneaked up and crashed the door shut.

CLICK!

GOT HIM! I'LL KEEP WATSON LOCKED IN HERE UNTIL AFTER THE GAME!

Mr Creep scuttled off to see the Sports Master—

I'M AFRAID WATSON'S FEELING UNWELL, BUT I'LL VOLUNTEER TO PLAY IN HIS PLACE!

GOOD CHAP!

Meanwhile—

THAT'S MICKI'S PET MONKEY! I'LL TEMPT IT OVER WITH A TOFFEE!

GOOD, NOW IT'S WITHIN REACH—

CHEW!

I'LL STICK A NOTE IN ITS COLLAR, ASKING FOR HELP!

THAT'S IT! OFF YOU GO TO SEE MICKI, YOUR MASTER.

Winker's clever idea worked, and Micki was soon reading the note—

WINKER'S LOCKED IN THE WOODSHED! I'D BETTER DASH ALONG AND LET HIM OUT!

So—

LUCKY FOR ME THAT CREEPY LEFT THE KEY IN THE LOCK! THANKS, MICKI!

Winker then asked Micki about the animals he had brought along.

ALL THESE ANIMALS ARE IN THE CIRCUS FOOTBALL TEAM!

GOSH! CAN I RIDE TO THE PITCH ON BIMBO, THE ELEPHANT?

LET'S GO, BIMBO!

But, at the pitch—

IT'S CREEPY, IN A GREYTOWERS STRIP! OO-ER! AND BIMBO REMEMBERS THAT CREEPY GAVE HIM A NASTY PROD WITH HIS CANE.

Bimbo strode over and picked up the terrified Creepy in his trunk.

HO-HO! BETTER PUT HIM DOWN, BIMBO!

HELP!

HA-HA! RIGHT IN THE DUCK POND!

GLUB!

SPLADOOSH!

Winker changed into his football gear in record time.

TWO MINUTES TO KICK-OFF! I'M JUST IN TIME!

What a super game it was! The Greytowers pupils and staff had several outstanding players, but the circus team also had excellent footballers, who could do clever tricks with the ball. At length, Winker jinked his way past several defenders and crashed a great shot into the net.

FREE FRUIT

EH? MY LUCKY DAY!

MUNCH! CHOMP! GUZZLE!

FRUIT

HERE COMES THE STALL-HOLDER. HIPPO'S FOR IT NOW!

THANKS, HIPPO! THAT WAS A SACK OF OLD FRUIT I WAS GOING TO TAKE TO THE DUMP. YOU'VE SAVED ME THE TROUBLE!

Shortly—

UNDER 10 YR OLDS ONLY

MY NEXT SIGN WILL REALLY LAND HIPPO IN THE SOUP.

HAW-HAW!

ALL WELCOME

In goes Hippo—

ALL WELCOME

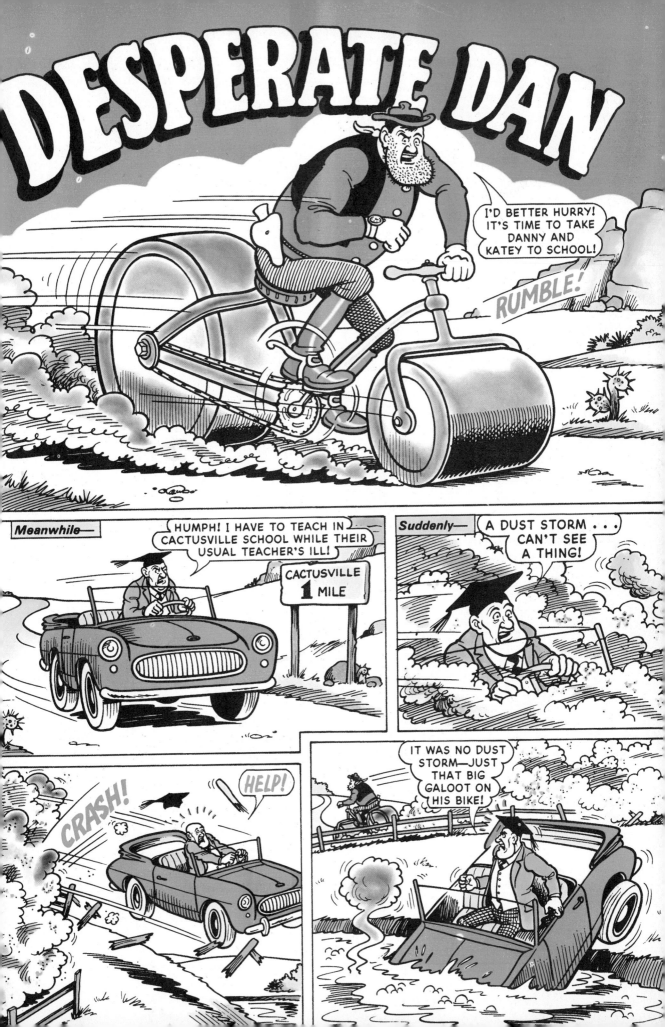

THERE!

DRAG!

THANKS, UNCLE DAN!

WE'VE BROUGHT SOME PRETTY FLOWERS FOR THE NATURE TABLE, SIR!

SWIPE!

PUNY LITTLE THINGS! BRING SOMETHING BIGGER!

OLD PARKY

Back home—

SO, YOUR TEACHER WANTS SOMETHING BIGGER? WELL, I KNOW THE VERY THING!

THIS SMELLY SKUNK WILL TEACH THAT BULLYING TEACHER A LESSON!

PONG!

NATURE TABLE

Shortly—

THERE'S A STRANGE SMELL IN HERE!

I DON'T WANT THAT HORRID LITTLE CREATURE IN MY ROOM!

FOUL BREATH!

I CAN'T STAND THE SMELL OF HIS BREATH!

NOW BRING SOMETHING **BIGGER** FOR THE NATURE TABLE!

NATURE TABLE

Dan makes another delivery—

I HOPE **THIS** IS BIG ENOUGH!

Then—

EH? WHAT'S THIS?

SNARL!

NATURE TABLE

LOOK AT HIM RUN!

HE'S TERRIFIED!

SCHOOL

SWISH!

SHOVE OFF!

I'VE NEVER SEEN A GIANT GRIZZLY BEAR SO FRIGHTENED!

THE TEACHER KEEPS PICKING ON US, UNCLE DAN! HE'S TOLD US TO BRING SOMETHING BIGGER STILL FOR THE NATURE TABLE!

IS THAT SO?

Next day—

AND WHAT PUNY LITTLE ITEM HAVE YOU PUT ON THE NATURE TABLE TODAY?

OH, JUST A LITTLE OLD . . .

SCHOOL

PARKY

HAM AND Egghead

I'M OFF TO VISIT OUR HEADMASTER! I'M SUCH A CLEVER PUPIL, I'LL MAKE A BIG IMPRESSION!

I'LL COME WITH YOU AND MAKE A BIG IMPRESSION, TOO!

HUH! SOME HOPES!

RUBBISH TIP

COULD YOU RACE ME TO THE CORNER, EVEN IF YOU WERE PUSHING THAT OLD PRAM?

EASILY!

PHEW! I THINK EGGHEAD'S OUTSMARTED ME!

HO-HO! I TOLD YOU I'D REACH THE CORNER FIRST!

PUFF! PANT!

Then—

LORRY DEPOT

I'LL SHOW YOU HOW STRONG I AM!

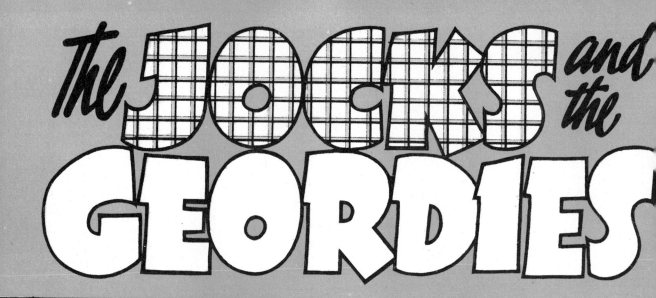

KORKY THE CAT

THIS RIVER'S FULL OF FISH, BUT IT'S FLOWING SO FAST I CAN'T CATCH ANY!

I'LL BUILD A RAFT!

NOW TO FETCH SOME ROPE!

Shortly—

EH? ALL MY LOGS HAVE GONE!

WAY IN ↓

I'LL BUILD A CAGE INSTEAD, AND LOWER IT ON TO THE RIVER BED!

NOW, I'LL NEED SOME NETTING!

Then—

I DON'T BELIEVE IT! MY OTHER PILE OF LOGS HAS DISAPPEARED TOO!

THOSE MARKS MUST HAVE BEEN MADE WHEN MY LOGS WERE DRAGGED AWAY.

Korky follows the trail—

'GAMEKEEPERS' TRAINING SCHOOL

HEY! WHAT'S THIS?

JUMP TO IT!

GAMEK... TRAINN...

SO **THAT'S** WHERE ALL MY LOGS WENT—TO BUILD A TRAINING CIRCUIT FOR NEW GAMEKEEPERS!

Just then—

HERE ARE THE MEN'S SNACKS!

INSTRUCT...

LAY THEM DOWN THERE, JUST NOW!

I WONDER WHAT'S IN HERE?

THEY TOOK MY LOGS SO NOW I'M HELPING MYSELF TO THEIR **CHOCOLATE LOGS!**

Strange Hill School

OH, HELLO THERE! AREN'T YOU A BIT SMALL TO BE COMING TO SCHOOL ON YOUR OWN?

MY MUMMY BROUGHT ME!

Eddie Potter is an ordinary schoolboy! In fact he's the ONLY ordinary schoolboy at a very strange school.

I JUST CAN'T GET USED TO THIS NEW PLACE AFTER GOING TO SCHOOL IN THE CITY!

THIS IS MY MUMMY!

ULP!

In class—

WELL, BOYS! WHAT WILL WE DO TODAY?

LET'S PLAY CRICKET, SIR!

CRICKET? WHAT'S THAT?

ER, IT'S A GAME, SIR! YOU NEED A BAT AND A BALL!

I HAVE A BAT!

OOH!

AND YOU CAN USE MY BALL!

GASP!

ER, MAYBE CRICKET'S NOT SUCH A GOOD IDEA!

WELL, HAS ANYONE DONE ANY PAINTINGS?

I PAINTED A PICTURE LAST NIGHT!

LET ME HAVE A LOOK!

IS IT A POSTER FOR A HORROR FILM?

NO! THE PICTURE'S CALLED "WHAT I DID ON MY HOLIDAY"! I SPENT LAST SUMMER AT UNCLE DRACULA'S CASTLE!

CLANG! CLANG!

YIKE! WHAT A DIN!

THAT'S THE DINNER BELL!

Then—

... LEG OF TOAD ... EYE OF NEWT ...

THAT MUST BE THE BIOLOGY CLASS IN THERE!

HELLO, DEARIE! WE'RE THE SCHOOL DINNER LADIES!

WAH!

In the dining hall—

I WONDER IF THAT METAL NUT IN TEACHER'S HEAD ...

... IS THE REASON HE BOLTS HIS FOOD?

CHOMP!

SLAP!

TEAR!!

GRIND

After lunch—

I'LL GO AND HAVE A WORD WITH THE HEAD! MAYBE HE'LL PUT ME IN ANOTHER CLASS!

COME IN, BOY! AS YOU CAN SEE, I'M THE **HEAD!** NOW WHAT CAN I DO FOR YOU?

ER...UM...NOTHING THANK YOU, SIR! I MUST BE GOING!

I WON'T LEARN ANYTHING IN THIS CLASS! I MIGHT AS WELL READ MY "DANDY"!

OH, NO! ALL MY CREEPY CLASSMATES ARE CLOSING IN ON ME!

WHAT ARE THEY GOING TO DO TO ME? I CAN'T BEAR TO LOOK!

PHEW! THEY ONLY CROWDED ROUND TO READ MY "DANDY"! MAYBE THEY'RE NOT SUCH A BAD CROWD AFTER ALL!

HOGG'S ANGELS

PORKY PERKINS →

← JASPER HOGG

BERT BACON →

ROAR!

VROOM!

LOOK AT THEM GO! HOGG'S ANGELS RIDE FAST AND ACT TOUGH!

ZOOM!

This guy is a DANDY reader!

THE DUSTY ROAD HAS MADE MY THROAT DRY AND THOSE ICED-LOLLIES LOOK MIGHTY JUICY!

THEY SURE DO, HOGG!

HAND OVER THOSE LOLLIES— RIGHT NOW!

BIFF! BAM! WALLOP!

OOH! HOGG'S ANGELS ARE SO ROTTEN THEY EVEN BEAT UP KIDS!

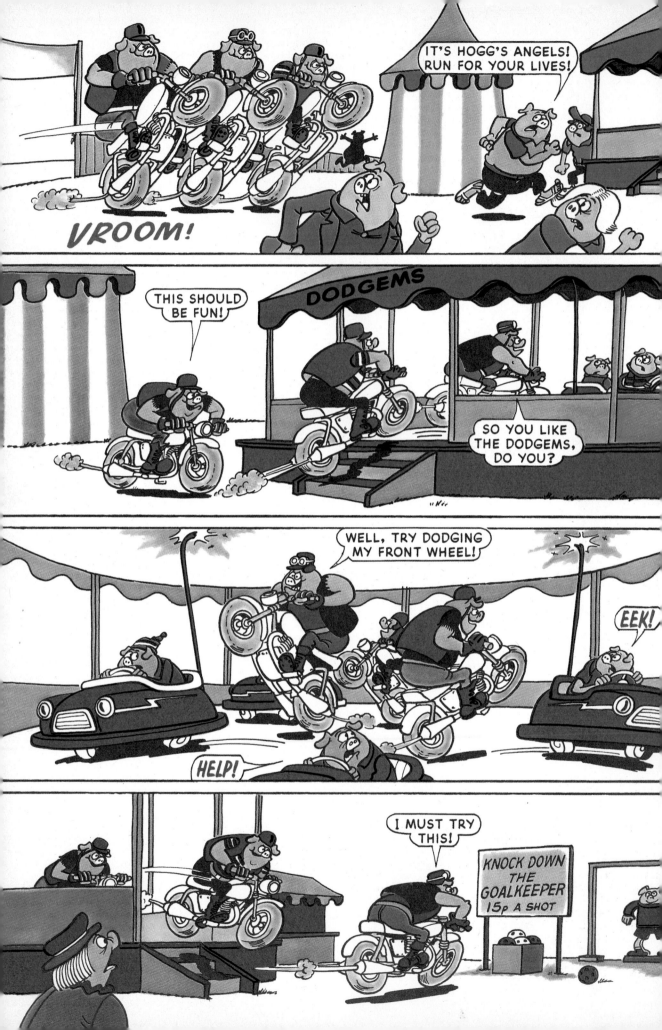

What wobbles and flies?—A " jelly "-copter!

PETER'S POCKET GRANDPA

ZOOM!

AH! WE'VE ARRIVED AT THE MAGPIE'S LAIR!

AND THIS IS ITS NEST—*OOF!*

NOW TO CUT MYSELF LOOSE!

CUT!

I HEAR FOOTSTEPS— I'D BETTER DODGE OUT OF SIGHT!

WHAT'S THIS? ANOTHER BANGLE? WELL DONE, MERLIN!

GOSH! IT'S NASTY NED, THE MONEY-LENDER!

I MUST PUT A STOP TO NASTY NED'S LITTLE GAME!

Outside—

WHERE'S HE GONE?

THERE HE IS—UP IN THAT TREE!

KEEP STILL, DAD, AND I'LL TRY TO REACH HIM!

I'M DOWN HERE! THAT'S ONLY A DUMMY IN THE TREE! NOW WATCH THIS!

PLUCK

YEAH! YEAH!

TICKLE

WAH!

WO-HO-HO! HA-HA-HA! HEE-HEE!

WHOOSH

BURRD'S GOT AWAY AGAIN!

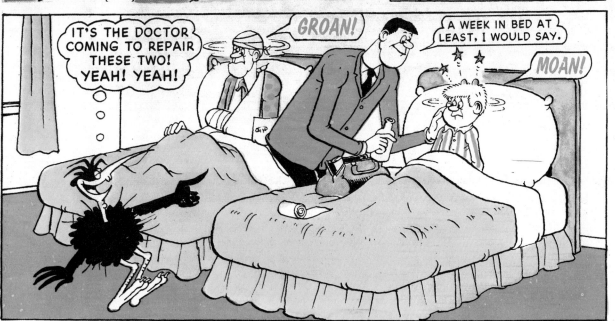

KORKY'S HISTORY

IN STONE-AGE TIMES, THINGS COULD BE ROUGH...

...WHEN CAVEMEN HAD A **BONE** TO PICK WITH EACH OTHER!

WHILE IN ANCIENT ROME, ARGUMENTS WERE USUALLY SETTLED BY PEOPLE TALKING...

...UNLESS SOMEONE REALLY HAD A **POINT** TO MAKE.

WHEN VIKINGS FELL OUT, A LONGBOAT...

...COULD BECOME TWO **SHORT** BOATS!

A SWORD WASN'T MUCH USE TO A KNIGHT, BECAUSE OF THE ARMOUR HIS ENEMY WORE...

...A TIN OPENER WAS MUCH BETTER!

WHEN NAPOLEON GAVE AN ORDER, HE DIDN'T EXPECT HIS MEN TO DO ALL THE FIGHTING...

...HE JOINED IN THE "SHOOTING" TOO!

BUT NOW WE LIVE IN GENTLER TIMES, WHEN GIRLS DISCUSS THINGS IN A LADYLIKE MANNER!

ER, MAYBE THINGS HAVEN'T REALLY CHANGED MUCH AFTER ALL!

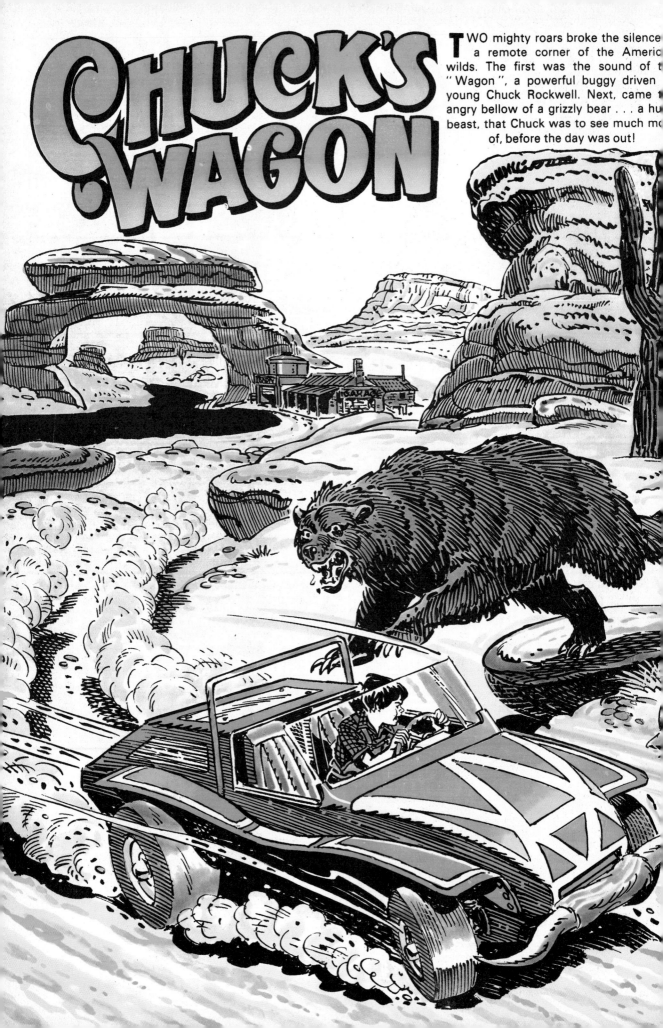

CHUCK'S WAGON

TWO mighty roars broke the silence
a remote corner of the Americ
wilds. The first was the sound of t
"Wagon", a powerful buggy driven
young Chuck Rockwell. Next, came t
angry bellow of a grizzly bear . . . a hu
beast, that Chuck was to see much m
of, before the day was out!

Our story starts earlier that day at the garage owned by Chuck's uncle, Pete.

THERE, CHUCK! I THINK YOUR BUGGY SHOULD BE READY FOR ACTION AGAIN!

THANKS, UNCLE PETE! I'M LOST WITHOUT MY WAGON!

TRY IT OUT, BUT BE CAREFUL TILL YOU'RE SURE IT'S OKAY!

A RUN OVER SOME ROUGH GROUND WILL PUT IT TO THE TEST!

UNCLE PETE'S A GREAT MECHANIC! THE WAGON'S GOING LIKE A DREAM!

But just then—

I DON'T BELIEVE IT! A WORLD WAR TWO FIGHTER PLANE, AND IT'S IN TROUBLE!

THERE'S THE PILOT! AND IT LOOKS AS IF HE COULD USE SOME HELP!

But the phone wasn't Pete's only way of reaching help! As the crooks sped off, the mechanic struggled to his feet and grabbed his C.B. radio.

CALLING CHUCK... CALLING CHUCK...

And in the Wagon...

...UNCLE PETE HERE! A COUPLE OF GUYS HAVE JUST ROBBED THE GARAGE! THEY'RE HEADING WEST!

Just then—

LOOK OUT! A SPEEDING CAR!

TWO GUYS IN A MIGHTY BIG HURRY! THAT'S THE CROOKS ALL RIGHT!

WE'LL NEVER CATCH THEM ON THE ROAD...

...BUT MY BUGGY CAN TAKE A FEW SHORT-CUTS OVER ROUGH COUNTRY!

As the crooks drew level with Chuck, a hail of bullets ripped along the side of their car.

And next instant—

LOOK! THE CROOKS WEREN'T HURT IN THE CRASH, AND THEY'RE ESCAPING WITH UNCLE PETE'S MONEY!

But just then— *ROAR!*

HELP! A GIANT GRIZZLY! THERE'S NO WAY I'M GOING ANOTHER STEP!

YOU WIN! WE'D RATHER GO TO JAIL THAN FACE THAT BEAST!

Back at the garage—

WE'LL SOON HAVE THESE TWO GUYS BEHIND BARS, BUT YOU'D BETTER SEE A DOCTOR ABOUT THAT ANKLE OF YOURS, MISTER!

YOU DON'T HAVE TO WORRY ABOUT ME, WHEN CHUCK'S AROUND WITH HIS WAGON!

POLICE

HIGHWAY PATROL

HARRY and his HIPPO

HO-HO! DRESSING UP IN OLD CLOTHES IS GREAT FUN!

WE'RE JUST LIKE MUSKETEERS!

Here comes Mum—

HOI! STOP THIS FOOLING AROUND!

IF YOU WANT SOMETHING TO DO, CARRY THESE BOXES TO THE TOWN HALL!

TOWN HALL

TOWN HA

OKAY, MUM!

I'M HELPING TO ORGANISE A FASHION SHOW TODAY!

TOWN HALL

Watch out, 'ippo!

BUMP!

TOWN HALL SIDE ENTRANCE

OWCH!

TOWN HALL

CRUNCH!

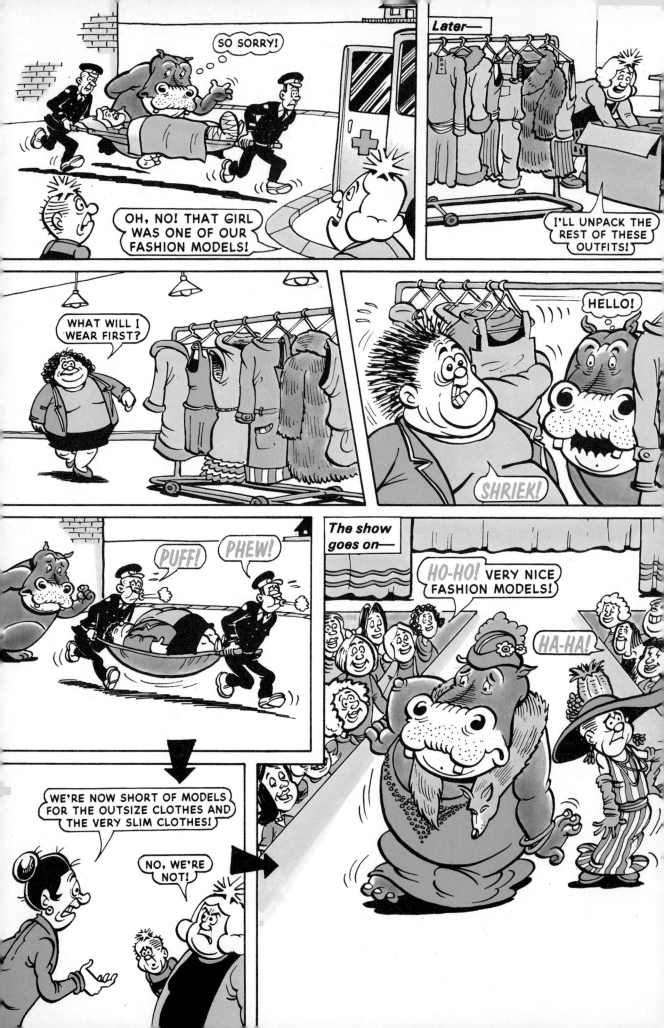

YEAH! UP YOU GO!

YAHOO!

BDOYING!

HA-HA! I'VE BEEN RIGHT EVERY TIME SO FAR!

ANOTHER MUG—ER, I MEAN—CUSTOMER. PLEASE COME IN!

I SEE YOU ARE GOING TO BE VERY POPULAR WITH YOUR PALS TODAY.

KICK ME

GREAT SMASHE

BUT NOT IN THE WAY HE THINKS! HO-HO!

KICK ME

THAT'S IT FOR THE DAY. I'VE DONE ENOUGH FORTUNE-TELLING!

SMAS
THE C
BALL G
FORT
TO

But, in the house—

GURR! I'VE HAD NOTHING BUT COMPLAINTS ABOUT SMASHER AND HIS LATEST SCHEME!

GULP! THAT'S DAD'S VOICE!

OOH! FOR ONCE I CAN SEE THE FUTURE, AND I DON'T LIKE THE LOOK OF IT!

KORKY the CAT

GYMNA[SIUM]

LET'S HAVE SOME SPARRING PRACTICE!

THUMP

I MADE YOU SEE DOUBLE, KORKY!

OOH!

When Korky recovers—

THAT'S NOTHING! I CAN MAKE DESPERATE DAN SEE DOUBLE!

YOU MUST BE JOKING!

WELL, BRING DAN TO THE GYM AT TWELVE O'CLOCK AND I'LL SHOW YOU!

Then—

THIS IS THE SHOP I WANT!

THERE'S DAN WAITING FOR ME!

MNASIUM

I HAD THIS KORKY T-SHIRT MADE SPECIALLY! AND NOW DESPERATE DAN IS SEEING DOUBLE!

YUP! I SEE TWO KORKYS!

I'VE BEEN TRICKED!

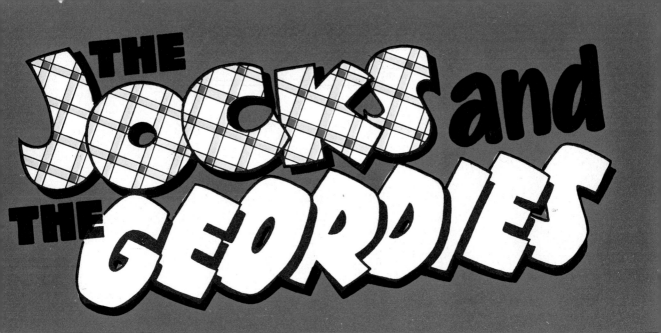

THE JOCKS and THE GEORDIES

LOOK, GEORDIES! I'VE FOUND A COPY OF TODAY'S DAILY BUGLE!

LET'S BASH THOSE JOCKS!

NO, WAIT! LISTEN TO THIS! THE DAILY BUGLE HAS PUBLISHED A TREASURE MAP AND CLUES IN A COMPETITION . . .

DAILY BUGLE
TREASURE MAP
COMPETITION—
FOLLOW THE CLUES
AND MAP INSIDE
TO FIND A
SPECIAL PRIZE
BURIED BY
THE DAILY BUGLE

ANYONE WHO FOLLOWS THE MAP AND CLUES HAS THE CHANCE OF FINDING A PRIZE BURIED BY THE NEWSPAPER. WHY DON'T WE GET THE JOCKS TO FOLLOW A SPECIAL TREASURE MAP MADE BY US— FOR A VERY SPECIAL PRIZE?

DAILY BUGLE
TREASURE MAP
COMPETITION

GREAT IDEA!

So—

I'VE MADE OUR SPECIAL MAP! NOW TO CAST IT ADRIFT IN THE RIVER.

HEE-HEE! FOR THE JOCKS TO FIND!

And downstream—

LOOK! A BOTTLE—AND THERE'S SOMETHING IN IT!

GOT IT!

OOH! WH-WHERE ARE WE?

LOOKS LIKE A CELLAR!

GOSH! LOOK AT ALL THAT OLD ARMOUR!

THIS IRON GLOVE FITS LIKE A . . . GLOVE! PERFECT FOR BASHING NOSES! AND THERE'S A FLIGHT OF STEPS OUT OF HERE!

Outside—

HAVE YOU SEEN THE GEORDIES?

YES! THEY ARE OVER IN THAT WOOD!

GET SOME ARMOUR AND FOLLOW US!

THERE THEY ARE! LET'S BASH 'EM!

EEK! LOOK!

CRUMBS!

GULP!

TWO GREAT MASTERPIECES

THE LAUGHING CAVALIER

THE LAUGHING COWBOY

YOU CAN WIN A DESPERATE DAN T-SHIRT AND JOIN DAN'S FANTASTIC CLUB! FIND OUT HOW IN THE DANDY WEEKLY COMIC—IT'S IN THE SHOPS EVERY TUESDAY!